The Parade
Sorting and Classifying

by Lynn Maslen Kertell
pictures by Sue Hendra and John R. Maslen

Scholastic Inc.
New York • Toronto • London • Auckland • Sydney • Mexico City • New Delhi • Hong Kong • Buenos Aires

The sun was shining on Parade Day.
Sally, Seth, and Tanner were excited.

They were going to march with
their favorite things.

Tanner liked the color blue.
He wanted to ride.

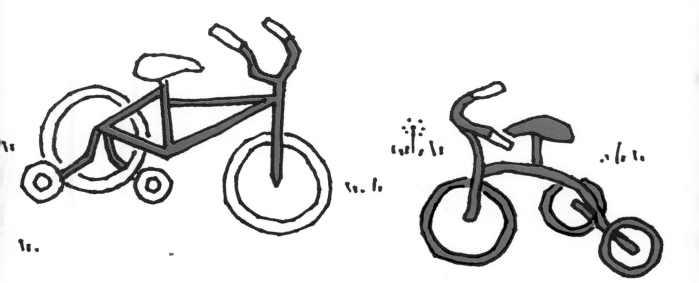

He adored things with three wheels.
What should he bring to the parade?

Tanner rode his tricycle.

Sally wanted something loud
and round. She loved to bang.

Sally chose a drum.

Seth felt happy. He wanted
something tall and cheerful
that waved in the breeze.

Seth picked a flag.

Rolling, banging, and fluttering,
the friends marched and marched.

It was the best parade ever!